Favorite Christmas Songs

Illustrated by
Barkat Curtin

Arranged by
Robert Pace

Copyright ©1997 by Lee Roberts Music Publications, Inc.
International Copyright Secured
ALL RIGHTS RESERVED
Unauthorized copying, arranging, adapting, recording or
public performance is an infringement of copyright.
Infringers are liable under the law.

Deck The Hall

With spirit

WELSH

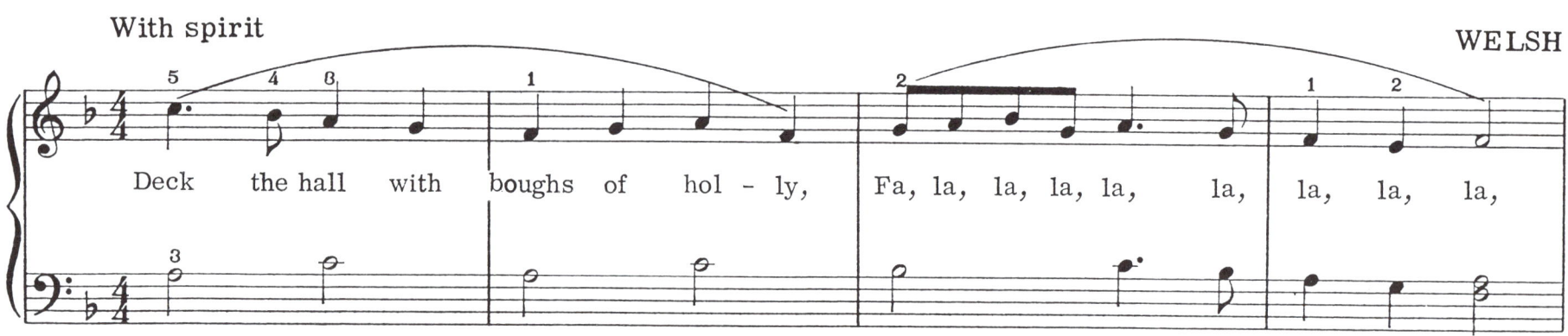

Deck the hall with boughs of hol-ly, Fa, la, la, la, la, la, la, la, la,

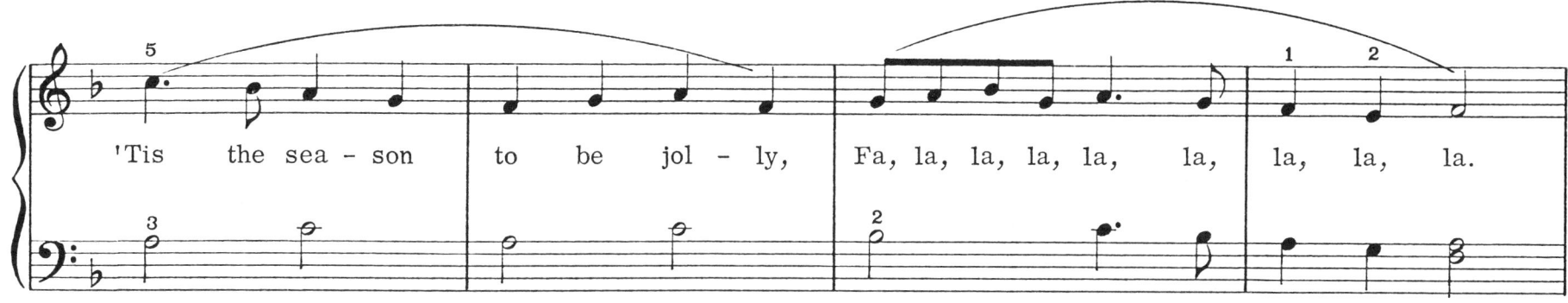

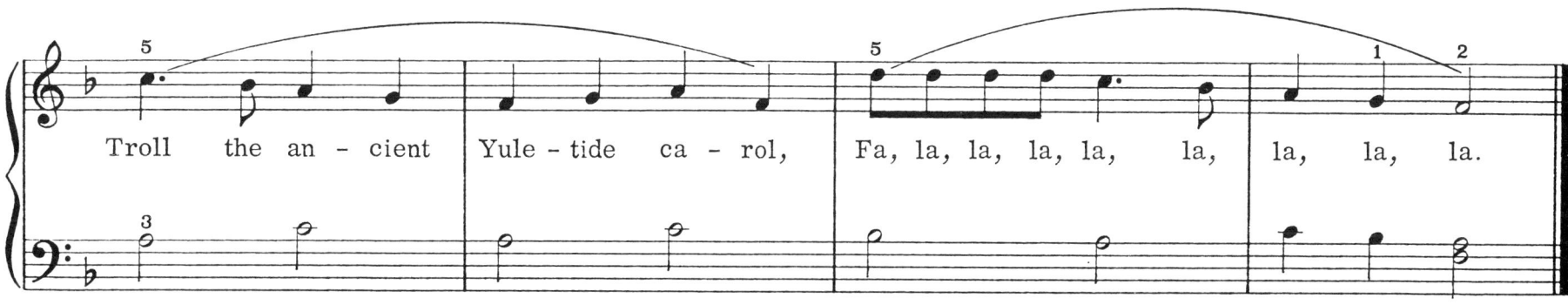

Up On the House Top

Joyfully

B.R. HANBY

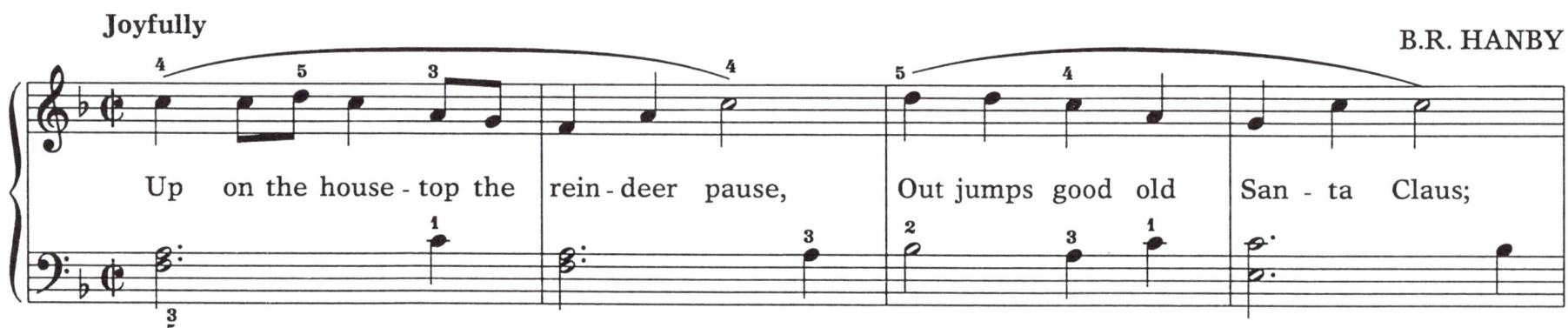

Up on the house-top the rein-deer pause, Out jumps good old San-ta Claus;

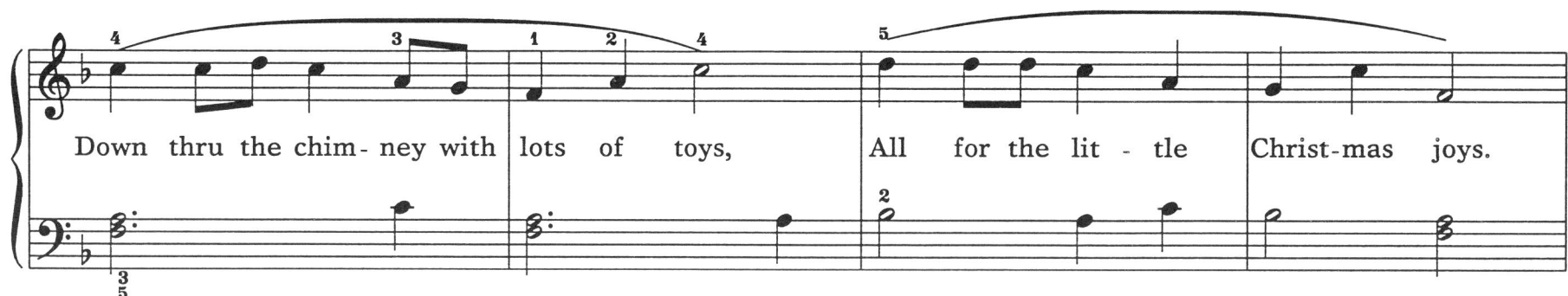

Chorus

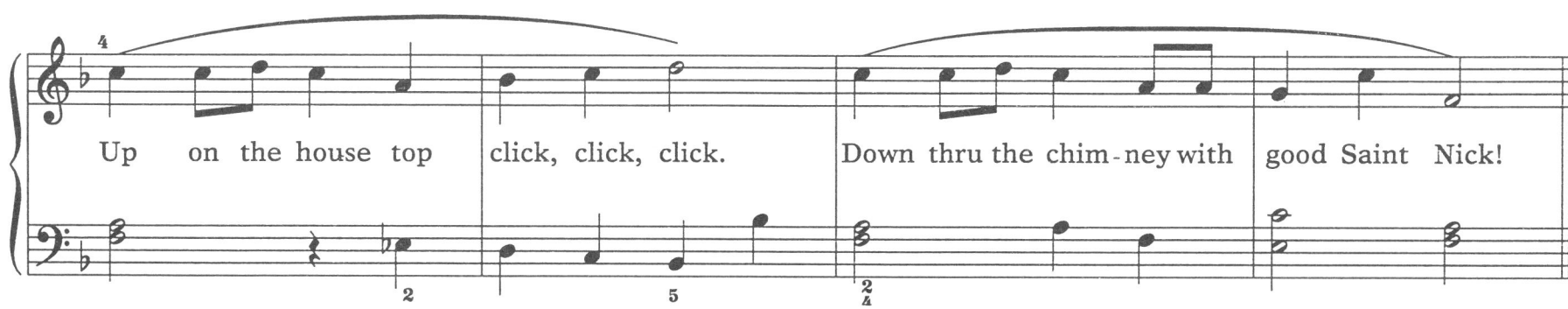

O Little Town of Bethlehem

PHILLIPS BROOKS
Slowly

LEWIS H. REDNER

O lit-tle town of Beth-le-hem, How still we see thee lie! A-bove thy deep and

dream-less sleep The si-lent stars go by; Yet in thy dark streets shin-eth The

ev-er-last-ing Light; The hopes and fears of all the years Are met in thee to-night.

We Three Kings of Orient Are

JOHN H. HOPKINS
Majestically

JOHN H. HOPKINS

We three Kings of Orient are, Bear-ing gifts we tra-verse a-far, Field and foun-tain, moor and moun-tain, Fol-low-ing yon-der star.

Chorus

O, Star of won-der, Star of night, Star with roy-al beau-ty bright, West-ward lead-ing, still pro-ceed-ing, Guide us to Thy per-fect light.

The First Noel

Moderately

ENGLISH

The first No - el, the an - gels did say, Was to cer - tain poor shep - herds in

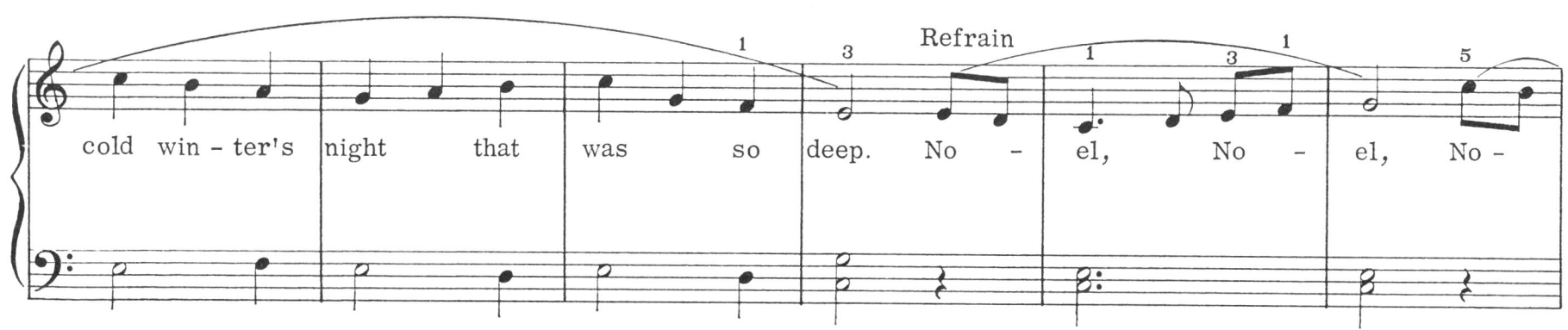
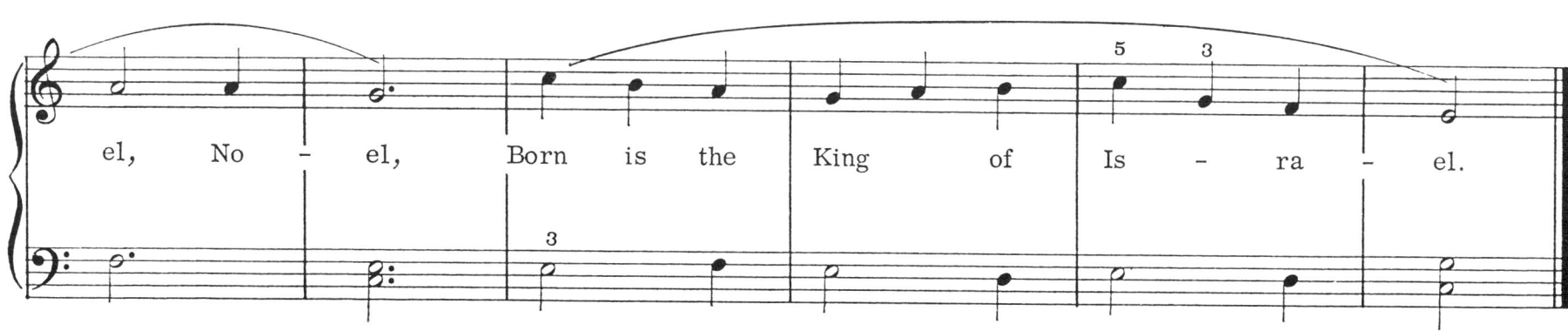

Away In A Manger

MARTIN LUTHER
Slowly

CARL MUELLER

A - way in a man - ger, No crib for a bed, The lit - tle Lord Je - sus laid down His sweet head, The stars in the sky looked down where He lay, The lit - tle Lord Je - sus, A - sleep on the hay.

I Saw Three Ships

With motion

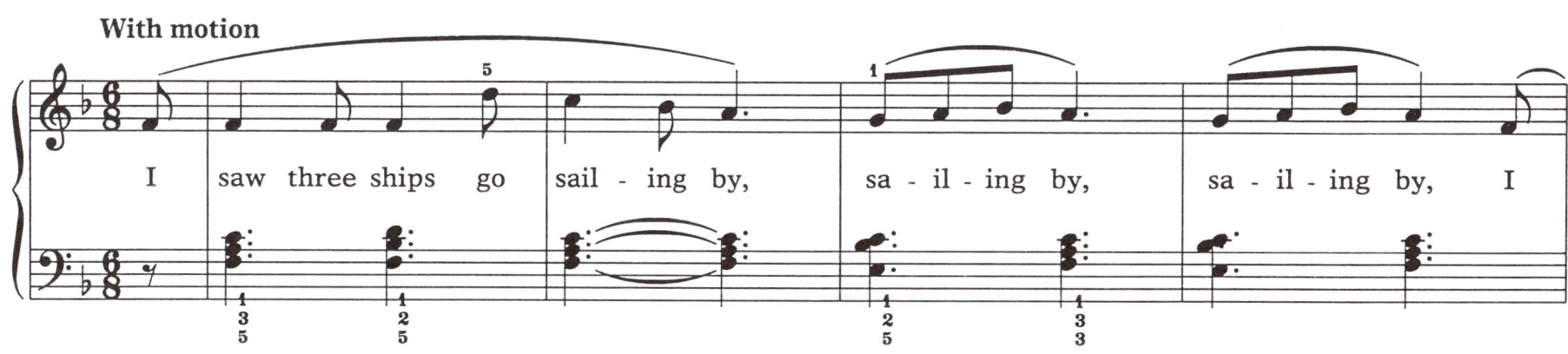

I saw three ships go sail-ing by, sa-il-ing by, sa-il-ing by, I

saw three ships go sail-ing by, on Christ-mas Day in the morn-ing.

When a poor man came in sight, Gath-'ring win-ter fu - el.

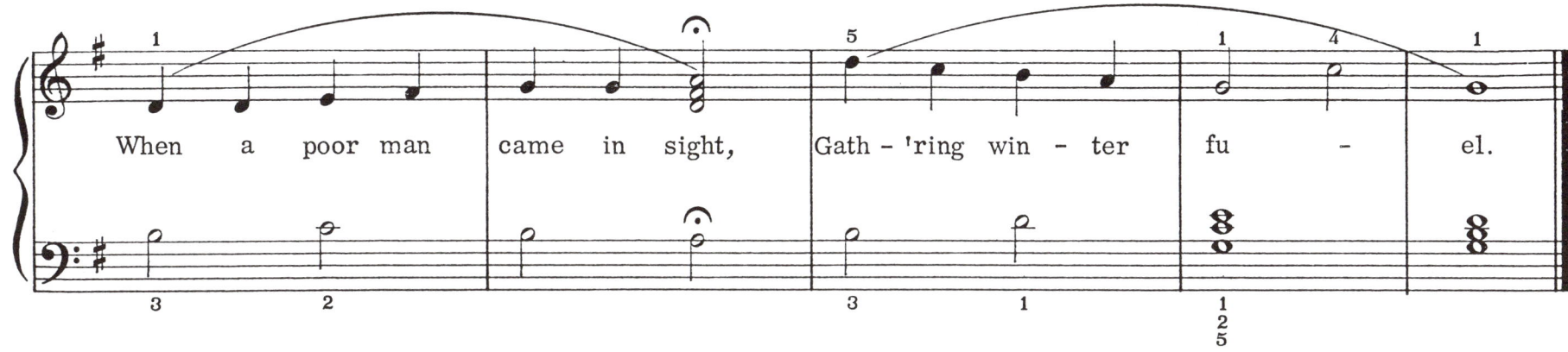

Joy To The World

ISAAC WATTS
Joyously

GEORGE F. HANDEL

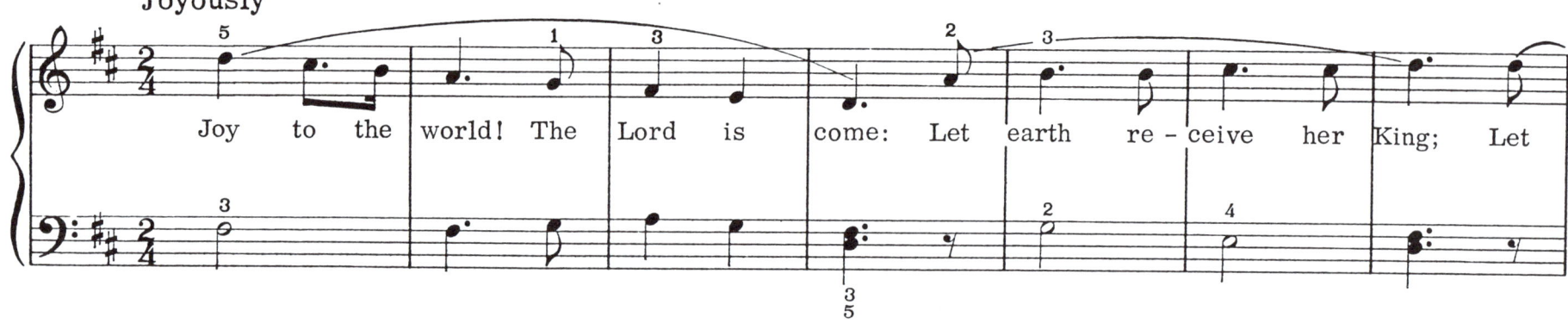

Joy to the world! The Lord is come: Let earth re-ceive her King; Let

ev - 'ry heart pre-pare Him room, And heav'n and na-ture sing, And

heav'n and na - ture sing, And heav'n, and heav'n and na - ture sing.

O Christmas Tree

H. L. P.

GERMAN

O Christ-mas tree, O Christ-mas tree! Our hearts should e're en - dea - vor,
O Christ-mas tree, O Christ-mas tree! Thy mes-sage to re - mem - ber.
If win-ter's bleak and

snow should fall, Thy lov-ing branches shelter all. O Christmas tree, O Christmas tree, Thy light will shine forev - er.

O Come All Ye Faithful

17th Century Latin Hymn
Trans. by F. Oakley

JOHN READING

O come, all ye faith-ful, joy-ful and tri-umph-ant, O come ye, O come ye to

17

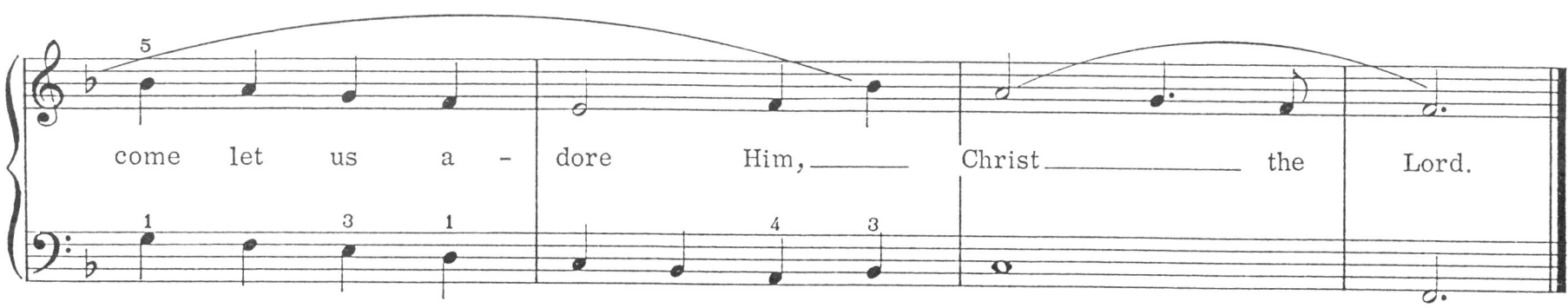

Silent Night

JOSEPH MOHR
Quietly

FRANZ GRUBER

Si - lent night! Ho - ly night! All is calm, all is bright, Round yon Vir - gin Moth-er and Child

Ho - ly In - fant so ten-der and mild, Sleep in heav-en-ly peace, Sleep in heav-en-ly peace!

We Wish You A Merry Christmas

TRADITIONAL WORDS
Gaily

ENGLISH

Jolly Old Saint Nicholas

Jol - ly old Saint Nick - o - las, Lean your ear this way!

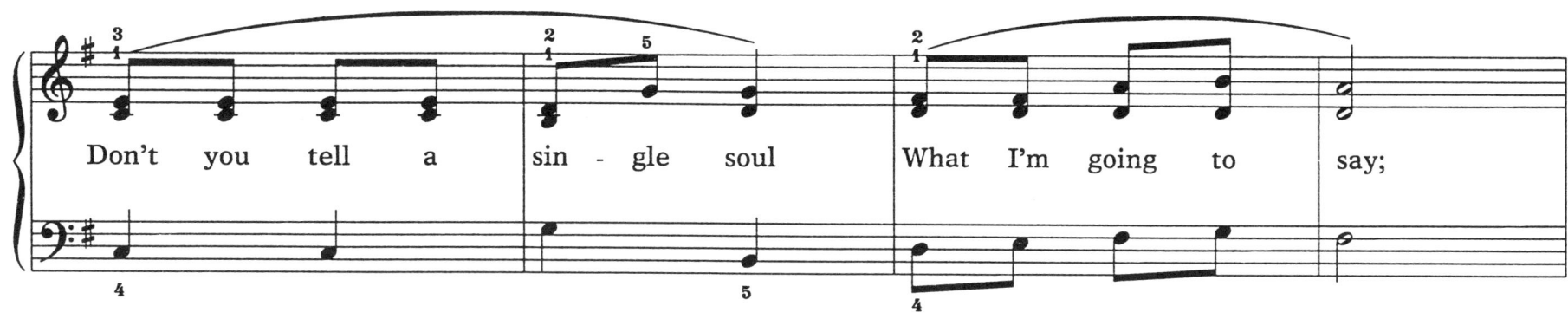

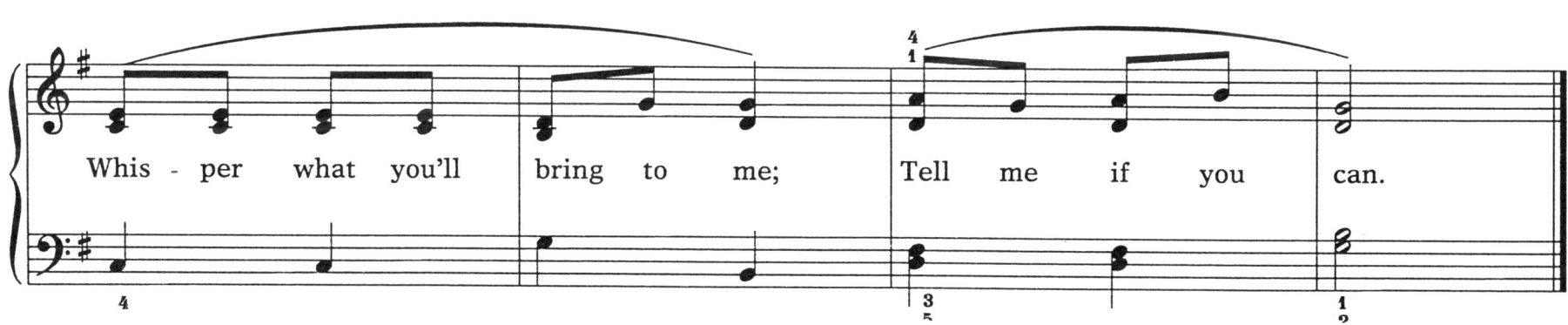

Jingle Bells

J. PIERPONT

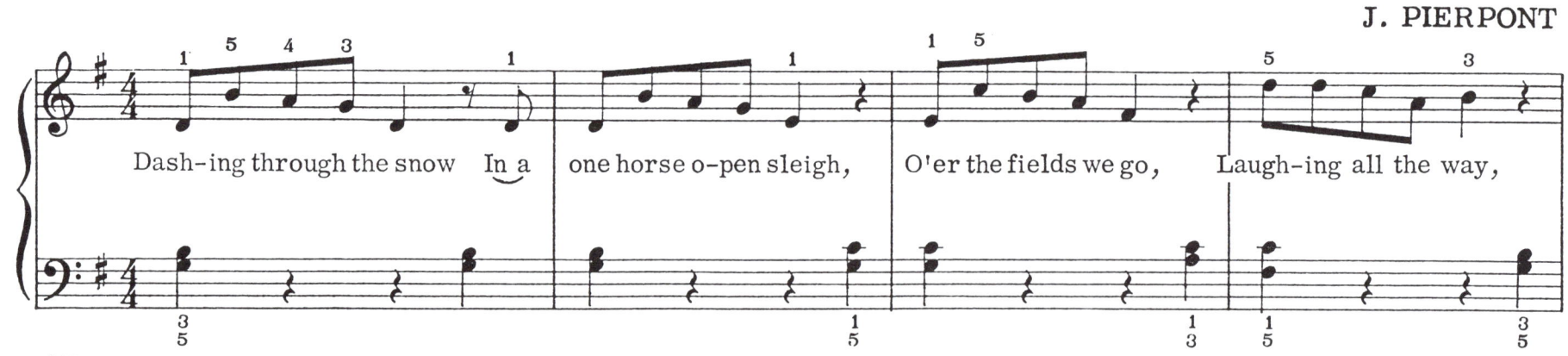

23